TRANSFER TESTS

GW00392627

Practice Test 1.

Read the following instructions carefully.

1. Study each question thoroughly before answering.

2. Answer the questions carefully.

3. Try to be aware of the time allowed for the test.

4. If you have difficulty with a question don't waste time.
    Move on and then return to those questions with which
    you had difficulty.

5. Make sure to check your answers.

6. Any working out should be done on a separate sheet of
    paper.

7. The test lasts one hour.

PUPIL'S NAME _____

TOTAL	
out of 58	

CEA Practice Test 1.

1 to 7.   Read the poem and answer the questions which follow.

ALL IN A DAY'S TOIL

Saturday morning, frosty with dew,
The day is cold, the spuds are new,
With baskets in our arms we trudge up the field,
Hoping to enlarge on our weekly yield.
No time to breathe or look around,
Our backs are bent, heads touch the ground,
All day long that digger goes,
The driver, he keeps us on our toes.

As morn wears on, we wait in vain,
It's past our tea time---he's late again.
At last I hear, " The tea's arrived,"
There's nothing as good as being revived.
The bread and jam is like roast ham,
The fresh brewed tea's like wine,
But I wouldn't call a spud field
The greatest place to dine.

At last the day has come to an end,
No more could I stoop or lift or bend.
We gather around to receive our pay,
I love it when it comes to the end of the day.
We go home contented despite the pain,
But when Saturday comes we'll be here again.

1.   In the **first verse** the gatherers are kept **"on our toes"**.
Who kept them on their toes ?

The driver

2.   **What** did they eat for tea ?

Bread and Jam and tea

3.   a.   What did they **"wait in vain"** for ?

For there tea

b.   What do the gatherers **hold** in their arms ?

_____baskets_____

4.   Which of the following **best describes** the **mood** of the poet in the **first** verse ? Tick (√) your answer.

happy and spirited............ ☐   tired and frustrated.... ☑

caring and conscientious... ☐   angry and depressed.. ☐

5.   Find the word **closest in meaning** to each of the phrases below. The words are in the **first verse**.

walk with a heavy step   _____trudge_____

total spuds gathered   _____

make bigger   _____enlarge_____

6.   At the end of the day which **3 things** will the poet no longer do ?

_____stoop   lift   or   bend_____

7.   Which **pair** of words below best express the **emotions** of the poet in the last verse ? Tick (√) your answer.

annoyance and fear..... ☐   joy and relief.... ☐

relief and annoyance... ☑   fear and joy....... ☐

8.   A girl who earns **£100** per week is getting an increase of **10%**.
How much extra will she earn in a week ?   £ ___10___

9.   James sells carrot plants at **5 pence** a plant.
How many plants would you get for **£3.50** ? _70____ plants

$5\overline{)3.50}$

10. If **2%** of my money is **£3** how much would **22%** of my money be ?   £ _____

11 to 13. The Pie Chart shows the outcome of a **survey** of the favourite TV programmes of a group of children.

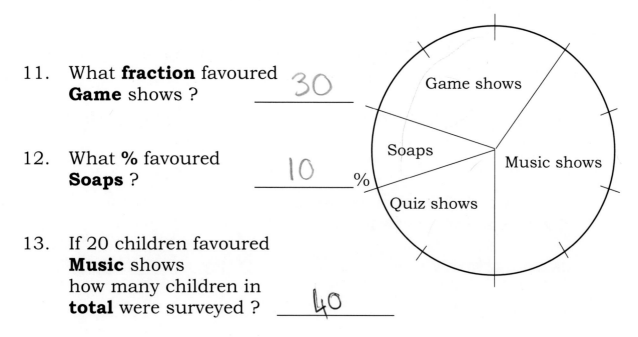

11.   What **fraction** favoured **Game** shows ?   _30_

12.   What **%** favoured **Soaps** ?   _10_ %

13.   If 20 children favoured **Music** shows how many children in **total** were surveyed ?   _40_

Mountain Ash School went on a Day Tour. The graph shows the amount spent by 6 of the children.

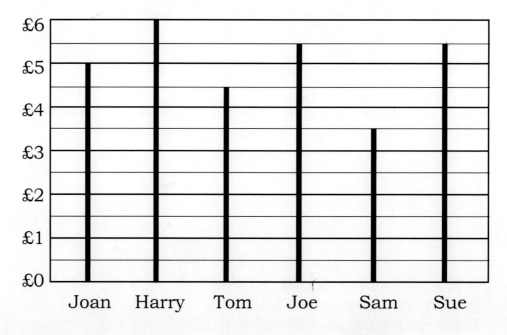

14.   Who spent **£1.50 more** than Tom ?   _Joe_

15.   How much did Joe and Sue spend **altogether** ?   £ _11.50_

3.

16. Harry had **£24** that morning. What **%** of this did he spend ?   ___25___ %

17. Joan spent **50%** of her savings on the day. How much savings had she before the day began ?   £ ___10___

18. If **654 - p = 376** what is the value of **p** ?   **p** = _____

19 to 25. **Read the following passage and answer the questions.**

   Richard could hardly eat for excitement, while Osmond hastily made his arrangements, belting on his sword and giving Richard a dagger to put in his belt. He placed the provisions in his wallet and then told Richard to lie down on the straw which he had brought in. "I shall hide you in it," he said, " and carry you through the hall, as if I was going to feed my horse."
   From the interior of the bundle Richard heard Osmond open the door. Then he felt himself raised from the ground and Osmond was carrying him downstairs. The only way to the outer door was through the hall, and here was the danger. Richard heard loud singing and laughter, as if feasting was going on; then someone asked, " Tending to your horse, sir ? "

19. In **what** were the provisions carried ?

_____

20. How were Richard and Osmond **armed** ?

_____

_____

21. **What** lay between Richard's room and the outer door ?

_____

_____

4.

22. Find the words in the passage which are **closest in meaning** to the following :-

a.   encircling his waist.................._____

b.   the inside.................._____

c.   supplies of food.................._____

23. Look at the first paragraph. Which phrase tells us that Osmond was **'planning in a hurry'** ?

_____

24. **In what** was Richard hidden when he was **smuggled**

out of the castle ?   _____

_____

25. At the end of the passage someone asked **"Tending to your horse, sir ?"**. What was meant by this ? Tick (√) your answer.

saddling/riding the horse............................. ☐

going to feed the horse............................. ☐

selling the horse............................. ☐

26. **37%** of the pupils in a class are boys.
What **percentage** of the class are girls ?   _____%

27. What will **8** brass screws cost if
100 brass screws cost **£15** ?   £_____

28. Andrew is **1$\frac{1}{2}$ m.** tall. Tom is

17 cms taller. How tall is Tom ?   _____m _____cms

29. A sack of potatoes weighs **10 kgs**. A shopkeeper took
3$\frac{3}{4}$ kgs and **2$\frac{1}{4}$ kgs** out of the sack. What **weight** of
potatoes was **left** in the sack ?   _____kgs.

5.

30. **Mary went to the Fun Park where the prices for the rides were as follows :-**

Mary got **£4** from her uncle. She went on the bumpers **twice**, the swings **three** times and on the horses **once**.

RIDES	
Bumpers	**50p**
Rocket	**40p**
Swings	**30p**
Horses	**30p**

How much money had she left ?   £ _____

31. The **area** of a square is **100 square centimetres**.

What is the **perimeter** of this square ?

_____ cms

32. If **1679 ÷ 23 = 73** fill in the missing numbers below.

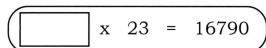

73 x 23 = ☐   ☐ x 23 = 16790

33. **Two thirds** of my savings is **£16.**
What is **three quarters** of my savings ?   £ _____

34. **Simplify** the following fractions.

a. $\dfrac{10}{15}$ = ☐   b. $\dfrac{8}{12}$ = ☐   c. $\dfrac{9}{21}$ = ☐

35. In a class $\dfrac{3}{4}$ of the children stay in school for lunch. If **12 children** go home for their lunch, how many stay at school ?   _____ children

36. **137** red flowers and **165** yellow flowers were made into bunches of **9** flowers.
How many flowers were left over ?   _____ flowers

6.

37 to 41. **Read the passage and answer the questions.**

The Giant's Causeway were one of the wonders of	*line 1*
Ireland and this famous beauty spot is in County	*line 2*
Antrim. Every year many tourists visit it.	*line 3*
People long ago believed that it was made by an	*line 4*
Irish giant called Fionn. The legend tells us that he	*line 5*
tried to build a raised road or causeway across the sea	*line 6*
to Scotland. According to the story this road was never	*line 7*
finished. The Giant's Causeway marks its starting point.	*line 8*
But of course this is only a story. What really	*line 9*
happened was quiet different. Millions of years ago	*line 10*
molten rock poured out. It spread through the earth's	*line 11*
crust like a river. As it cooled, it hardened into	*line 12*
rock and formed. Pillars on the Antrim coast.	*line 13*
There are more than 38,000 pilars in the Giant's	*line 14*
Causeway, many of which are over ten metres high.	*line 15*
Most of these pillars are six-sided and fit closely	*line 16*
together. Many of them form unusual shapes , some	*line 17*
looking like houses cut from the rocks. One of these	*line 18*
unusual shapes is called the Wishing Chair while	*line 19*
the most famous is the Giant's Bed.	*line 20*

Tick (√) A, B, C or D for each of the following :-

37. A **full stop** and a **capital letter** are incorrectly used in

A.   line 1 ☐   B.   line 3 ☐

C   line 13 ☐   D.   line 18 ☐

38. The correct spelling of **"quiet"** in line 10 is

A.   quiit ☐   B.   queit ☐

C.   qiuet ☐   D.   quite ☐

39. There is a **spelling mistake** in

A.   line 2 ☐   B.   line 7 ☐

C   line 14 ☐   D.   line 20 ☐

7.

40. Which word in line 1 is used **incorrectly** ?

 A. Giant's ☐ B. were ☐

 C one ☐ D. wonders ☐

41. The words **raised** in **line 6** and **molten** in line 11 are

 A. verbs ☐ B. adjectives ☐

 C nouns ☐ D. pronouns ☐

42. One farmer had **127** sheep. A second farmer
had **6 times** that number. **How many** sheep
did the second farmer have ?   _____sheep

43. Mark had **43** marbles one morning. During
that day he won **19** marbles and lost **11**.
How many marbles had he then ?   _____marbles

44. If the **last day** of September is on a **Saturday**
on what day would **October 8th** be ?   _____

45. If **December 11th** was on a **Tuesday** on
which day would Christmas day fall ?   _____

How many lines of symmetry have each of the shapes below ?

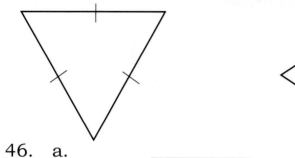

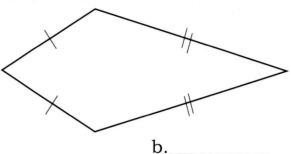

46.   a. _____   b._____

47.   If the shape **on the left** is turned **180°** in which position will it be ? Tick (√) the correct shape.

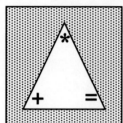      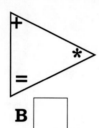   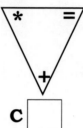   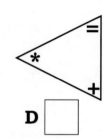

A ☐   B ☐   C ☐   D ☐

48.   I bought **55** oranges at **30** pence each.
I used a **calculator** to calculate the total cost in **£'s**.
Tick (√) the calculation I used.

30 x 55 ☐   55 x 0.03 ☐   55 x 0.3 ☐

49.   Write **135 minutes** in hours and minutes.   _____ hrs _____ mins.

50.   A clock shows this time :-   **13 : 30**

Tick (√) the **12-hour time** which corresponds to **13:30**.

1.30 am ☐   3.30 am ☐

1.30 pm ☐   3.30 pm ☐

51.   Underline the **longest** length.

6.66 m   66 cm   6666 mm   0.66 m

9.

52 to 58. Read the poem and answer the questions which follow.

The beauty of the world has made me sad,
This beauty that will pass,
Sometimes my heart has shaken with great joy
To see a leaping squirrel in a tree,
Or a red ladybird upon a stalk,
Or little rabbits in a field at evening,
Lit by a slanting sun,
Or some green hill where shadows drifted by,
Some quiet hill where mountainy man has sown
And soon would reap, near to the gate of heaven,
Or children with bare feet upon the sands
Of some ebbed sea, or playing on the streets
Of little towns in the land,
Things young and happy.
And then my heart has told me:
These will pass,
Will pass and change, will die and be no more,
Things bright and green, things young and happy,
And I have gone upon my way
Sorrowful.

52. Name an **insect** which the poet enjoys.

_____

53. On what did **"shadows drift by"** ?

_____

54. Which of the following statements are **TRUE** ?
Tick (√) your answers.

A. my heart shook with happiness............................. ☐

B. the squirrel was jumping over the hill.................... ☐

C. children were playing in the sand........................ ☐

D. the towns were large....................................... ☐

10.

55. Write **TWO verbs** from the first three lines of the poem.

_____   _____

56. The following is a **summary** of the poem. <u>Underline</u> the most appropriate word in each set of three words **(in bold type)** which makes this summary **most accurate**.

The poem has **no   a few   many** rhyming words and **only one**

verse   no verses. It begins and ends in a **joyful   melancholy**

angry manner with the poet using his **ears   nose   heart** to

convey to the reader the marvel of beauty.

57. In the last five lines of the poem what two things will **"pass and change"** ?

_____

_____

58. Which of the following **best describes** what the poet is writing about in the poem ? Tick (√) your answer.

...memories of his work..................................... ☐

...times of poverty... ☐

...his memories in old age.................................. ☐

...the thoughts of his friends.............................. ☐

11.

TRANSFER TESTS

Practice Test 2.

<u>Read the following instructions carefully.</u>

1.   Study each question thoroughly before answering.

2.   Answer the questions carefully.

3.   Try to be aware of the time allowed for the test.

4.   If you have difficulty with a question don't waste time. Move on and then return to those questions with which you had difficulty.

5.   Make sure to check your answers.

6.   Any working out should be done on a separate sheet of paper.

7.   The test lasts one hour.

PUPIL'S NAME _____

TOTAL	
out of 58	

CEA Practice Test 2.

1 to 7.   **Read the poem and answer the questions which follow.**

I will arise and go now, and go
    to Innisfree,
And a small cabin build there, of clay
    and wattles made:
Nine bean-rows will I have there,
    a hive for the honey-bee,
And live alone in the bee-loud glade.

And I shall have some peace there,
    for peace comes dropping slow,
Dropping from the veils of the morning
    to where the cricket sings;
There midnight's all a glimmer, and noon a
    purple glow,
And evening full of linnet's wings.

I will arise and go now, for always
    night and day
I hear the lake water lapping with low
    sounds to the shore;
While I stand on the roadway, or on the
    pavements grey,
I hear it in the deep heart's core.

1.   Which of the following words means the same as **cricket** in the **second verse** ? Tick (√) your answer.

a game ☐   an insect ☐   a judge ☐

2.   Which of the following has the same meaning as **"full of linnet's wings "** in the **last line of verse 2** ?
Tick (√) your answer.

birds were being plucked................... ☐

birds were flying................................ ☐

feathers were floating in the air........... ☐

3. How would the words, **bean-rows**, **bee-loud** and **honey-bee** in the **first verse** be described ? Tick (√) your answer.

collective.......☐   compound...☐

hyphenated...☐   abstract.......☐

4. The **4 phases** of a day are mentioned in the **second verse**. What are these 4 phases ?

_____

5. Two words in the second verse mean the same as **gleam**. Write these **TWO words** below.

_____   _____

6. From where does **"peace drop"** in the second verse ?

_____

7. Write out **the line** in the last verse which tells us that the poet is **in a city** when he wrote the poem.

_____

8. Write as decimal fractions.

a. $\dfrac{9}{10}$ = ☐   b. $\dfrac{5}{10}$ = ☐   c. $\dfrac{4}{5}$ = ☐

9. What is the **value** of the **underlined digits** in these numbers ?

2 <u>7</u> 4 . 6   1 7 . 6 <u>3</u>   1 2 3 . <u>8</u>

_____   _____   _____

10. Complete the fractions below.

a. $\dfrac{4}{5}$ = $\dfrac{☐}{10}$ b. $\dfrac{4}{5}$ = $\dfrac{12}{☐}$

11. a. How many $\frac{1}{2}$'s in $4\frac{1}{2}$?   _____ halves

b. How many $\frac{1}{4}$'s in $2\frac{1}{2}$?   _____ quarters   2.

12. a. How many **grams** in 2 . 8 kilograms ? _____ grams

    b. How many **kilograms** in 12,000 grams ? _____ Kgs.

13. Which of the following is the **"odd-one-out"** ?
    Tick (√) the correct answer.

14. A bag of crisps costs **23p**. How much would
    you pay for **100 bags** of crisps ?   £ _____

15. Bottles of cranberry juice hold **1 . 5 litres**.
    How many **millilitres** would there be in
    3 bottles of cranberry juice ?   _____ mls

16. What are the **missing terms** in this sequence :-

    a. **3,   8,   _____,   _____,   23,   28.**

    b. Write the **missing terms** in this sequence :-

       3.5,   3.0,   _____,   _____,   1.5,   _____.

17. What is $\frac{3}{4}$ of £200 ?   £ _____

18. A clock shows this time :-   **17 : 30**

    Tick (√) this time on the **12-hour clock**.

    7.30 am [ ]   5.30 am [ ]

    7.30 pm [ ]   5.30 pm [ ]

                              3.

19 to 25. **Here is a page from a publication.**
Answer the questions which follow.

JANUARY   2009

1.   **Thursday**   (Bank Holiday)
No school today.   Slept late in the morning.
Went shopping with Mammy,   bought toys.   Great dinner.
Saw a film in the cinema.   Phoned Mary.

JANUARY

2.   **Friday**
Up early.   Went to Granny to help her.   Took her shopping.
Had a great time.   She gave me money.
Slept over at Granny's house.   My friend Joan stayed.
Played board games.

JANUARY

3.   **Saturday**
Got up early.   Made Granny her breakfast.   Went to Alice's house to
play on her computer.   Stayed till evening.
Went home,   watched Cookstart on TV,   tired,   Bed early.

JANUARY

4.   **Sunday**
Started my school project.   Went out and took photos of trees,
hedges and flowers;   went to shops with Mammy.   Continued project.
Minded Gary, neighbour's child. He was very good. Finished project.

JANUARY

5.   **Monday**

---

19.   **Name** the publication from
which the above page was taken.   _____

20.   Ann owns this page. She had a
dental appointment on **January 9th**.
On what **day** was her appointment ?   _____

21.   Which **activity** did Ann do with **both**
her Mammy and her Granny ?   _____

4.

22. **On which day** did Ann
    have a great meal ?   _____

23. **On which day** of the week was
    Christmas Day 2008 ?   _____

24. On which of **these topics** was Ann carrying out her project ?
    Tick (√) your answer.

    animals ☐   food ☐   plants ☐   computers ☐

25. Written in the boxes below are words with **similar meanings**
    to some of the words used in the passage. **Write out the words
    from the passage that have similar meanings.**

completed		assignment		looked after

    ↓   ↓   ↓

26. **100** bars of chocolate cost **£36**.
    How much would **25** bars cost ?   £_____

27. Complete the following mathematical sentences :-

    a.   19 x 24 = 38 x [   ]

    b.   [   ] x 36 = 50 x 18

28. Work out the following :-
    £ 0 . 76 x 10   +   £ 0 . 38 x 100   £ _____

29. Coats are **reduced** by **25%** in a sale.
    How much would you **pay** for a coat
    which cost **£120** before the sale ?   £ _____

30. A cup and three saucers cost **£4**.
    If a saucer costs **80 pence**
    how much is the cup ?   £ _____

5.

31. In a sale all items are reduced by **20 %**. How much will I **save** if I buy **3 carpets** which would have cost **£100 each** before the sale ?

£ _____

32. A carpenter charges **£15 an hour**. How much would he get for **20 minutes** work ?

£ _____

33. The **weights** of 4 children are :-

16 . 25 kgs   **17 . 5 kgs**   **15 . 75 kgs**   **16 . 9 kgs**

What is their average weight ?

_____ kgs

34. Tickets cost **£1 for 12**. How many would you get for **25 pence** ?

_____ tickets

35. A floor measures **700 cms** long and **700 cms** wide.

What is the **area** of the carpet ?
Tick (√) your answer.

28 sq. metres ☐   490 sq. metres ☐

49 sq. metres ☐   4.9 sq. metres ☐

36. The Pie Chart shows the **colours** of cars produced in a factory in a month. There was a total of **120** cars produced in this month.

a. How many **Green** cars were produced ?

_____

b. How many **Black** cars were produced ?

_____

c. What **fraction** of the cars were **Blue** ?

_____

6.

Read the passage and answer the questions.

"Sit down, Jackson."   *line* **1**
The Boss's tawny-grey head was still leaning   *line* **2**
over the papers on his desk while Jackson studied   *line* **3**
him. It was easier to view the Boss's face now   *line* **4**
that the photo of his deceased son was no longer   *line* **5**
on the desk. Poor Mattie Jones! Everyone realised   *line* **6**
that the tiny crippled boy would never grow up but   *line* **7**
his father, Bert Jones, had never believed it.   *line* **8**
Jackson felt a sadness for Mr. Jones in a way.   *line* **9**
The Boss had spent thousands upon thousands of   *line* **10**
pounds trying to save his son You couldn't be too   *line* **11**
sorry for him because he was a hard man. He fired   *line* **12**
people, who didn't live up to his harsh standards,   *line* **13**
without affording them a second chance. Except for   *line* **14**
his son, sucess was the only thing which counted.   *line* **15**
"Jackson," the Boss snapped as he lifted his   *line* **16**
head, " your department has paid its way this   *line* **17**
past year and we don't keep things that don't   *line* **18**
pay. It's finished. I'm sorry but you're through here."   *line* **19**
          Tick (√) your answers.

37.   A **full stop** is missing in

      A.   line 3 ☐   B.   line 7 ☐

      C   line 11 ☐   D.   line 13 ☐

38.   The word **has** on line 17 is used **incorrectly**.
      Which of the following words is the **correct** one ?

      A.   had ☐   B.   hasn't ☐

      C   have ☐   D.   haven't ☐

39.   Which of the words on line 5 is an **adjective** ?

      A.   son ☐   B.   longer ☐

      C   photo ☐   D.   deceased ☐

40. The word **sucess** is incorrectly spelt on line 15.
Which of the following is the **correct** spelling ?

      A.   success ☐   B.   suces ☐

      C   succes ☐   D.   succees ☐

41. The words **'snapped'** and **'lifted'** on line 16 are in the

      A.   plural ☐   B.   past tense ☐

      C   future tense ☐   D.   present tense ☐

20 m

42. This garden has a **2 metre** wide path around the **lawn**.

14 m

What is the **Area** of the lawn ?

_____sq. metres

43. What is the **Perimeter** of the lawn ?   _____ metres

44. What is the **area** of the **shaded part** of this shape ?

Each square is 1 square cm. ▨

_____sq. cms.

8.

45. If I arrive at school at **8 . 25 am** and
    class starts at **9 . 00 am** how
    long have I to wait for class to begin ?   _____ minutes

46. Calculate the following angles.

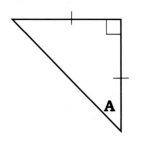
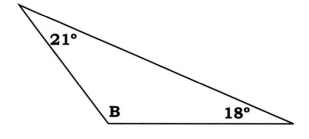

    Angle **A** = _____ °   Angle **B** = _____ °

47. Which is the **ODD-ONE-OUT** ? Tick (√) your answer.

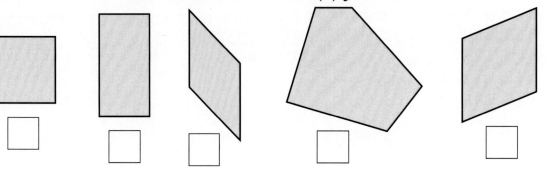

48. a.

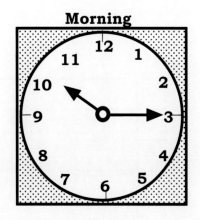

    Morning

    This clock is **25 minutes fast.**

    Write the **correct time**
    using am or pm.

    _____

    b.   A TV programme lasted from **9 . 55 pm to 10 . 35 pm**.

          How many minutes did it last ?   _____ minutes

49. The time shown on the clock is **5.10 pm.**
All clocks move in a clockwise
direction.
What time will it be when the
minute hand moves through **180°.**

_____ pm

50. John played **10 games** on his Playstation.
His **lowest** score was **3** and the range of his scores was **7.**
His **mean** (average) score was **5.**

a.   What was John's **highest** score ?   _____

b.   What was John's **total** score ?   _____

51. The **night** temperature in Belfast in January was **-5° C**.
The temperature during the day was **6° C.**
By **how many degrees** did
the Belfast temperature **rise** ?   _____°C

52 to 58.   **Read the poem and answer the questions.**

I live in Stone Age years
And now I've overcome my fears
On how to defend myself from beasts
With a flint spear by which I kill
This no doubt will make a feast.

I will use its hide to make my clothes
While my wife will sit and sew
We also eat a meal of bread and fish
Which is served in a hollowed flint dish.

In my cave I have protection
From wild animals I sent in some direction
It gives me shelter from the weather
And stores berries and nuts we gathered.

For cooking and warmth we have a fire
Which we light using wood and stone
And use to roast our meat
And also gives us out its heat.

10.

52. Which word in the **third verse** tells us
    the poet lived in **primitive times** ? _____

53. **What** was used for lighting a fire ?

_____

54. **Flint** was used to make **TWO articles** mentioned in the poem.
    What are these **TWO articles** ?

_____

55. The words **cooking** and **warmth** are used in the last verse.
    What **part of speech** are these words ? Tick (√) your answer.

    verbs ☐   nouns ☐   adjectives ☐   pronouns ☐

56. Name the **FIVE** foods that are mentioned in the poem.

_____

_____

57. Which of the following are the words **years, fears and beasts**
    as used in the first verse ? Tick (√) **TWO** answers.

    past tense ☐   plurals ☐   compound words ☐

    adjectives ☐   verbs ☐   nouns ☐

58. This is a **summary** of the poem. In the summary there are
    groups of **three words** from which to choose.
    Underline the **most appropriate** word from each group which
    makes the summary an **accurate** version of the poem.

    The poem is set in   **a city   the countryside   a cave** which

    gives the occupants **protection   safety   warmth** from wild

    beasts and **shelter   direction   storage** from the rain and

    sun. Only **two   three   four**   people are mentioned in the

    poem and one of these is   **a child   a woman   a grandparent**.

11.

CEA   Test 1.   ANSWERS

1. the driver   **2**. bread and jam   **3**. **a**. for the tea
   b. baskets   **4**. tired and frustrated   **5**. **a**. trudge
   b. weekly yield **c**. enlarge   **6**. stoop, lift, bend
7. joy and relief   **8**. £10   **9**. 70 plants   **10**. £33
11. 3 tenths   **12**. 10%   **13**. 50   **14**. Harry   **15**. £11
16. 25%   **17**. £10   **18**. 278   **19**. wallet
20. dagger and sword   **21**. the hall   **22**. **a**. belting
   b. interior **c**. provisions   **23**. hastily made his arrangements
24. bundle of straw   **25**. going to feed the horse
26. 63%   **27**. £1.20   **28**. 1 m 67 cms   **29**. 4 kgs
30. £1.80   **31**. 40 cms   **32**. 1679,   730   **33**. £18
34. **a**. 2 thirds **b**. 2 thirds **c**. 3 sevenths   **35**. 36 children
36. 5 flowers   **37**. C-line 13   **38**. D-quite   **39**. C-line 14
40. B-were   **41**. B-adjectives   **42**. 762 sheep   **43**. 51 marbles
44. Sunday   **45**. Tuesday   **46**. **a**. 3   **b**. 1
47. A   **48**. 55 x 0.3   **49**. 2 hrs 15 mins   **50**. 1.30 pm
51. 6666 mm   **52**. red ladybird   **53**. some green hill
54.   A------my heart shook with happiness,
   C------children were playing in the sand
55. has made,   will pass,   has shaken (2 out of 3)
56. no, only one verse, melancholy,   heart
57. things bright and green,   things young and happy
58. his memories in old age

CEA   Test 2.   ANSWERS

1. an insect   **2**. birds were flying   **3**. hyphenated
4. morning, midnight, noon, evening   **5**. glow, glimmer
6. the veils of the morning   **7**. on the pavements grey
8. 0.9,   0.5,   0.8   **9**.   7 tens (70),   3 hundredths ($\frac{3}{100}$),
8 tenths ($\frac{8}{10}$)   **10**. **a**. 8 **b**. 15   **11**. **a**. 9 halves
b. 10 quarters   **12**. **a**. 2800 grams **b**. 12 kgs   **13**.
14. £23   **15**. 4500 mls   **16**. **a**. 13, 18
16. **b**. 2.5, 2.0, 1.0   **17**. £150   **18**. 5.30 pm
19. diary   **20**. Friday   **21**. shopping
22. Thursday   **23**. Thursday   **24**. plants
25. completed=finished, assignment=project, looked after=minded
26. £9   **27**. **a**. 12 **b**. 25   **28**. £45.60   **29**. £90
30. £1.60   **31**. £60   **32**. £5   **33**. 16.6 kgs
34. 3 tickets   **35**. 49 sq. metres   **36**. **a**. 45 **b**. 30 **c**. 1 quarter
37. C-line 11   **38**. B-hasn't   **39**. D-deceased
40. A-success   **41**. B-past tense   **42**. 160 sq. m
43. 52 metres   **44**. 22 sq. cms.
45. 35 mins.   **46**. A = 45°,   B = 141°   **47**.
48. **a**. 9.50 am **b**. 40 mins   **49**. 5.40 pm
50. **a**. 10 **b**. 50   **51**. 11°C   **52**. cave
53. wood and stone   **54**. spear, dish   **55**. nouns
56. bread, fish, berries, nuts, meat   **57**. plurals, nouns
58. a cave, protection, shelter, two, a woman

CEA Test 3. ANSWERS

1. leather apron   **2**. farmer   **3**. caressing the sole, I stroke the heel, there's beauty in this art of touch and feel (2 out of 3)

4. from the hot iron, from the forge fire   **5**. a female horse

6. **a**. rigorous   **b**. pail   **c**. cavity   **7**. **a**. tread   **b**. a noun

8. **a**. 26   **b**. 13   **9**. 21   **10**. 61 secs   **11**. 30

12. 3 tenths   **13**. 20%   **14**. 21 cms   **15**. 26 sq. cms

16. 17 sq. cms   **17**. A = 35°, B = 65°   **18**.

19. **a**. in search of food and water   **19**. **b**. oasis

20. palm, cactus   **21**. store food, store water, padded feet, long hair over the eyes (3 out of 4)   **22**. adjectives

23. they can store water in their stems   **24**. dunes, waves

25. **a**. dunes   **b**. store   **c**. originates   **d**. prolonged   **26**. A

27. equilateral   **28**. line c   **29**. £4   **30**. **a**. 09:35   **b**. 22:10

31. 12 . 50 pm   **32**. 45   **33**. 48   **34**. 31   **35**. 9000

36. 97   **37**. B-adjective   **38**. B-line 9

39. D-was proven   **40**. B-decorations   **41**. B-their

42. 54 . 11   **43**. 25   **44**. 23 metres   **45**. 10, 5, 2.5

46. **a**. x = 12   **b**. y = 5   **47**. **a**. a = 77   **b**. d = 44 **48**. 7 . 45 pm

49. 10 balls   **50**. **a**. 12   **b**. 23   **51**. 34.6 kgs

52. **a**. True   **b**. false   **53**. geographers and navigators

54. he found no men to assist him in his own townland

55. from his studies   **56**. he thought he was a failure

57. adjectives   **58**. **a**. involved   **b**. prime   **c**. denied

CEA Test 4.   **ANSWERS**

1. repeat   **2**. **a**. Music and Movies,   Alan Talks **b**. 4
3. primary school pupils   **4**. YES   **5**. remake, classic, cast, adventure, suspense (3 out of 5)   **6**. B & W--black and white, 1956--made in 1956   **7**. MP--Alan talks, A chef--Cook with Cara
8. 30 years   **9**. r + s = s + r,   s x r = rs,   2r + s = s + r + r
10. **a**. €30 **b**. €200   **11**. **a**. £48 **b**. £640   **12**. 6, 3, 7
13. 200 mls   **14**. 54   **15**. 3 eighths   **16**. 100 times
17. 60°   **18**. **a**. 60° **b**. pentagon   **19**. **a**. foolish
b. amazed   **c**. on the railway platform   **20**. whistling, hooting,   shouting   **21**. funny kind of hat   **22**. Summer
23. people going to the seaside   **24**. compound
25. **a**. it was a warm day and people were going to the seaside
b. she didn't believe him at first or so much shouting
26. 19 bags   **27**. 5.95 kgs   **28**. 2 ninths
29. 2 hrs 15 mins   **30**. 1 hr 40 mins
31. 2 hrs 35 mins   **32**. 6 hrs 50 mins   **33**. 14th March
34. 23rd March   **35**. Tuesday   **36**. Sunday
37. C- line 11   **38**. B-nouns   **39**. C-to   **40**. C-line 9
41. B-calendar   **42**. 234   **43**. 100   **44**. 7 weeks
45. 0.5 metres   **46**. 10 sq. metres   **47**. 48 tenths
48. 77.4 kgs   **49**. 26   **50**. 33   **51**. £100
52. proper noun   **53**. some very small streets
54. Joseph knew the route as well as Pierre   **55**. faithful
56. trustworthy   **57**. **a**. True **b**. False **c**. True **d**. False
58. city, a few, thirty, fifteen

TRANSFER TESTS

Practice Test 3.

Read the following instructions carefully.

1. Study each question thoroughly before answering.

2. Answer the questions carefully.

3. Try to be aware of the time allowed for the test.

4. If you have difficulty with a question don't waste time. Move on and then return to those questions with which you had difficulty.

5. Make sure to check your answers.

6. Any working out should be done on a separate sheet of paper.

7. The test lasts one hour.

PUPIL'S NAME _____

TOTAL	
out of 58	

CEA Practice Test 3.

1 to 7.   **Read the poem and answer the questions which follow.**

Give me the hammer anvil and nail
The old leather apron, the bellows and pail
Avail myself of the tools of the trade
' Tis easier work than a pitchfork and spade.
So often I sit with a "clout" on my knee
This rigorous work of a blacksmith, that's me.
Caressing the sole, I stroke the heel
There's beauty in this art of touch and feel
Many paths have been trodden and waterholes seen.
The foot is now sore where the shoe has been
Now I'll approach it with anvil and tap
The sweat of my brow drops on to my lap.
The puff of the bellows, the shower of the sparks,
The mare's tail swishes, like a fast moving shark,
Into the pail goes the shoe cavity.
Measured for size it fits perfectly.
I gaze o'er the half door to watch as the mare
Goes galloping off with the finest pair
Of golden shoes that were ever seen
' Cause the mare is mine
And to me she's QUEEN.

1.   What **protective clothing** did the blacksmith wear ?

_____

2.   To what **occupation** is the phrase **" a pitchfork and spade"**
      referring ? Tick (√) your answer

        mechanic ☐   farmer ☐

        bricklayer ☐   carpenter ☐

3.   Write out the two **lines** in the poem which tells us that the
      blacksmith's work was a **'labour of love'**.

_____

_____

4. From where do you think the **"shower of sparks"** came ? Tick (√) **TWO** answers.

from the anvil ☐   from the hot iron ☐

from the forge fire ☐   from the bellows ☐

5. On which of the following is the blacksmith **fitting shoes** ? Tick (√) your answer.

a male horse ☐   a shark ☐

a donkey ☐   a female horse ☐

6. Find the words in the poem which have **similar meanings** to the following :-

a. hard and demanding..............._____

b. bucket............................_____

c. hollow or gap....................._____

7. a. **Trodden** in line 9 is the **past tense** of which verb ?   _____

b. **"clout"** as used in **line 5** is

a noun ☐   a verb ☐   an adjective ☐

8. a. If you **double** the **difference** between **39** and **52** what number do you get ?   _____

b. If **three** times a number is **39** what is the **number** ?   _____

9. What is the **mean (average)** of the following numbers ?

17, 20, 16, 25, 23, 14, 19 and 34.   _____

2.

10. The following times were recorded by 4 runners in a race.
65 secs   63 secs   59 secs and 57 secs.
What was their **mean (average)** time ?

_____secs.

11 to 13.   The Pie Chart shows the names of **150 pupils** in a school who have **Pat, Mary, Sam, Ann and Liz** as their names.

11. **How many** pupils are called **Pat** ? _____

12. What **fraction** have the name **Liz** ? _____

13. What **%** of the pupils are called **Sam** ? _____%

14. What is the **Perimeter** of this shape ?

_____ cms

15. What is the **Area** of this shape ?

_____sq. cms

6.5 cms

4 cms

16. What is the **Area** of the

shaded part of this shape ?

Each square is

1 sq. cm.

1cm

1cm

_____sq. cms

3.

17. Calculate the following angles.

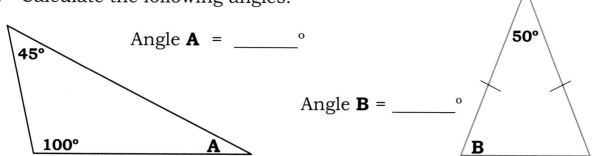

Angle **A** = _____ °

Angle **B** = _____ °

18. Which is the **ODD-ANGLE-OUT**.   Tick (√) your answer.

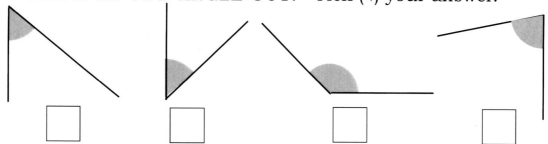

☐   ☐   ☐   ☐

19 to 25.   **Read the following passage and answer the questions.**

The desert is a hot dry place where little rain falls for months or even years. Few plants or animals can live in the desert. Plants such as the cactus do grow there because they can store water in their stems for a prolonged period.

In some parts of these arid lands water is found. This place is called an oasis where the water usually originates from an underground spring. Because of this palm trees and other plants survive.

Most deserts are sandy and as a result, when the winds blow, the dry sand piles up in heaps called dunes. The wind often moves the sand in waves across the desert. Sometimes sandstorms are caused when fierce gales blow blinding sand into the air.

Travelling across deserts is very hazardous and the camel is well suited to travelling across the desert. It is known as the 'ship of the desert' and it can store food in its hump and water in its stomach. It has padded feet to help it walk on the sand and long hair protects its eyes and nose from sandstorms.

The largest desert is in Africa and is called the Sahara. Some Arab tribes live there in tents and move from place to place with their camels, sheep and goats, in search of food and water.

19.   a.   Why do the Arab tribes **move about** in the deserts ?

_____

19. b. What is the **name** of the area in
         a desert where water is found ?_____

20. Write the **names** of a tree and a plant
     which grow in these areas ?

_____   _____

21. Give **three** reasons why camels are the **most**
     suitable animal for desert travel.

_____   _____

_____

22. What kind of words (**parts of speech**) are **prolonged**,
     underground and **fierce** ?

         _____

23. Why do cactus plants **survive** in the desert ?

_____

24. Into which **two shapes** does the wind blow the sand ?

_____   _____

         Find words in the story that mean :-

25. a. sandhills.............................. _____

     b. to keep things until needed......_____

     c. to begin or arises from............._____

     d. lengthened or extensive..........._____

26.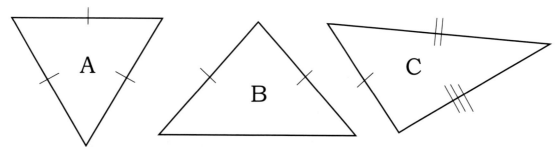

In which of these shapes are all the sides **equal** ? _____

27. What is the **name** of this triangle ? _____

28.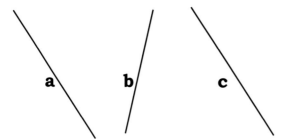

Which line is **parallel** to line **a** ?

Line _____

29. A piece of beef weighs **1.5 kgs**.

The cost of it was **£3**.

How much would **2 kgs** of this beef cost ? £_____

30. Write these times as **24-hour** times.

Morning

Evening

a. _____:_____   b. _____:_____

31. A football match kicked off at **11 . 20 am**. It lasted **1½** hours. **At which** of the following times did it **end** ? **Circle your answer**.

12 . 20 am   **12 . 50 am**   **12 . 20 pm**   **12 . 50 pm**

6.

32. **Triple** the **sum** of 3, 7 and 5. _____

33. What is **half** the **product** of 12 and 8 ? _____

34. What number is **halfway** between **17** and **45** ? _____

35. Subtract **1000** from **ten thousand**. _____

36. What is the **SUM** of 9^2 and 4^2 ? _____

37 to 41. **Read the passage and answer the questions which follow.**

Jethro's instinct were proven correct. Most of the	*line 1*
larger centres had already ordered their trees from	*line 2*
the huge plantations up in the mountains, which left	*line 3*
smaller centres, shops and supermarkets.	*line 4*
For two glorious days after the school holidays	*line 5*
began, they cut and sawed and carried the young	*line 6*
trees to the trailer, there gloves stiffening with resin	*line 7*
and sweat and frost, pine-needles sticking to their	*line 8*
clothes then began the slow journey to the shops on	*line 9*
icy roads, past country homes with coloured lights and	*line 10*
decorasions in windows, Jethro watching the	*line 11*
side-mirror to see that none of the trees toppled out.	*line 12*
The larger ones still remained in the plot and	*line 13*
between them, those open spaces which he would hog	*line 14*
to himself in the summer before he went away. It was	*line 15*
going to be an exciting time ahead during the rest of	*line 16*
holidays. There would be very many happy events	*line 17*
before he had to set off again for the city to pursue his	*line 18*
endeavours in the libraries and lecture halls.	*line 19*

Tick (√) your answers.

7.

37. What **"part of speech"** are the words **larger** in line 2 and **huge** in line 3 ?

A   verbs ☐   B   adjectives ☐

C   adverbs ☐   D   nouns ☐

38. There is a **capital letter** and a **full stop** missing in

A   line 1 ☐   B   line 9 ☐

C   line 14 ☐   D   line 18 ☐

39. The words **were proven** in line 1 are used incorrectly. The correct words are

A   shall proven ☐   B   will proven ☐

C   would proven ☐   D   was proven ☐

40. The correct spelling of **'decorasions'** in line 11 is

A   decorashuns ☐   B   decorations ☐

C   decoratons ☐   D   decarations ☐

41. The correct word for **there** in line 7 is

A   thier ☐   B   their ☐

C   they're ☐   D   theer ☐

42. What is the **sum** of the following numbers ?

3 . 45,   23 . 6   9 . 06   and   18

_____

43. Write the missing number.

$$8^2 + \underline{\hspace{2cm}} = 89$$

44. How many metres in **2300 centimetres** ? _____metres

45. Complete this **number sequence** :-

160, 80, 40, 20, _____ , _____ , _____

A **letter** can stand for an **unknown number**.
Work out **what number** each letter stands for in the following :-

46. a.   11 + **x** = 23   b.   72 x **y** = 360

   x = ☐   **y** = ☐

47. a.   **a** - 32 = 45   b.   396 ÷ 9 = **d**

   a = ☐   **d** = ☐

48. The drying time for varnish is between **2 and 4 hours**.
The varnishing of a mahogany door is completed by **3.45 pm**.

What is the **latest time** by which
the varnish will be dry ?   _____

49. A bag contains 4 **Blue** balls, 6 **Black** balls and a number of
Green balls.
There is a **50/50 chance** of picking a **Green** ball
out of the bag at random.

How many **Green** balls are in the bag ?   _____balls

50. a.   How many $\frac{1}{10}$'s are there in **1.2** ?   _____

   b.   How many $\frac{1}{10}$'s are there in $2\frac{3}{10}$?   _____

9.

51. Write **34,600 grams** in **kilograms**. Tick (√) your answer.

346 kgs ☐   3460 kgs ☐

3.46 kgs ☐   34.6 kgs ☐

52 to 58. **Read the poem and answer the questions.**

In 1451 Christopher Columbus was born
Genoa in Italy was Columbus' home town
And his studies convinced him the earth was round.

Geographers and navigators thought that
India could be reached by sailing west,
And Christoper Columbus was the man for the test.
He found no men to assist him in his own townland,
And so he decided to travel to Spain for a helping hand.

So for Spain he set out long and far
But Spain was involved in a costly war,
So again he was denied aid
But shortly after realised that progress was being made.
For King Ferdinand and Queen Isabella
decided to give their support.
And with that he got things ready and
his crew he did escort.

On August the 3rd 1492 Columbus set sail with his crew.
On the ships Pinta Nina and Santa Maria,
He went out to explore and came upon islands more.

Christopher Columbus who was in his prime
Had made some of the greatest discoveries of all time.
Christopher Columbus who was a famous sailor,
Died with the thought that he was a failure.

52. Write **TRUE** or **FALSE** for each of the following :-

a.   Christopher Columbus was born in Genoa.............._____

b.   Christopher Columbus was a famous soldier.........._____

10.

53. Who thought that **"India could be reached by sailing west"** ?

_____

54. Why did Columbus have to travel to **Spain** to **get help** for his trip ?

_____

55. How did Columbus know that the **"earth was round"** ?

_____

56. Columbus died feeling **disappointed**.
What made him feel like this ?

_____

57. What **"part of speech"** are the words **"helping"** in the second verse and **"costly"** in the third verse ?
Tick (√) your answer.

verbs ☐   adjectives ☐   nouns ☐   adverbs ☐

58. Write the words from the passage which are **closest in meaning** to the following :-

   a.   participating (third verse).........._____

   b.   at his best (last verse)................_____

   c.   refused (third verse).................._____

11.

TRANSFER TESTS

Practice Test 4.

Read the following instructions carefully

1. Study each question thoroughly before answering.

2. Answer the questions carefully.

3. Try to be aware of the time allowed for the test.

4. If you have difficulty with a question don't waste time. Move on and then return to those questions with which you had difficulty.

5. Make sure to check your answers.

6. Any working out should be done on a separate sheet of paper.

7. The test lasts one hour.

PUPIL'S NAME _____

TOTAL	
out of 58	

CEA Practice Test 4.

1 to 7. **Read the TV Schedule and answer the questions which follow.**

CHANNEL 1	CHANNEL 2
7.00 News and Weather	9.00 Education Time
7.15 Cartoons (R)	9.00--Basic History
8.00 Moonman Dan :-	9.45--Religions
Children's science	10.00-Art Facts
8.30 The Tales of the	11.00-News and Weather
Robot Dog (R)	11.05-Alan Talks :- Alan
9.00 Morning for Children.	reviews the week's
Action-packed menu	politics, politicians and
of sport, music, quizzes	events. Not to be
and celebrities.	missed.
11.00 Sports Arena	12.10-Cook with Cara :- The
11.00-Soccer	cookery programme
11.40-Rugby	for the amateur. (R)
12.00-Cricket	12.50 Film :- River Queen
1.00-Basketball	A strange but brilliant
1.30-Racing	love story. (1956 B & W)
2.00 News and Weather	2.15 News and Weather
2.15 Film:- East of Nowhere	2.30 Music and Movies :- A
an interesting remake	Review of current
of a 1953 classic of	music and film. All the
adventure and suspense.	gossip.
Very strong cast. (1996)	

1. The **abbreviation (R)** is used after a number of programmes. What does it stand for. **Circle** your answer.

      radio   **review**   **repeat**   **remake**

2.   a. Channel 2 has **Two review programmes** in its schedule. Name these Two programmes.

   _____

     b. How many **Weather forecasts** is it possible to watch between the two Channels ?

   _____

3. What **kind of person** is most likely to watch the
   first programme on Channel 2. Tick (√) your answer.

   sports enthusiast ☐   night-shift worker ☐

   primary school pupils ☐   university professors ☐

4. Pat enjoys watching films. Will he be able to watch **both** the
   Channel 1 film and the **Channel 2 film** without
   missing any part of either ? Circle either **YES** or **NO**.

   YES   **NO**

5. **Four Nouns** are used in the description of the Channel 1
   film "**East of Nowhere**".   Write **Three** of these Nouns below.

   _____ _____ _____

6. The bracket (**1956 B & W**) after the Channel 2 film **River
   Queen** tells us **2 Facts** about the film.
   What are **these facts** represented by **1956** and **B & W** ?

   _____

   _____

7. Write out the **name** of a programme where you would **most
   likely** find the following people :-

PERSON	TV PROGRAMME
Member of Parliament	
A Chef	

8. A young man's age is the **smallest number**
   which has 2, 3 and 5 as **common** factors.

   How old is this person ?   _____ years

2.

9.   Which **THREE** of the following mathematical sentences
       are **TRUE** ?   Tick (√) your answers.

       r + s = s + r   r - s = s - r

           r + s = rs   2r + s = s + r + r

           s x r = rs   r x s = s + r

10 & 11.   The chart below can be used to change **£ sterling**
           into **€ euro**. Using the chart answer the questions.

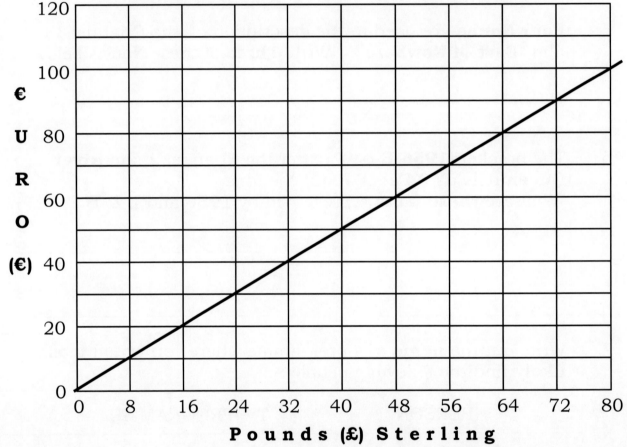

10. a. How many **€uro** would you get for **£24** ?   € _____

     b.   How many **€uro** would you get for **£160** ?€_____

11. a. How many **£ sterling** would you get for **€60** ?£ _____

     b.   How many **£ sterling** would you get for **€800**? £ _____

3.

12. Circle the **numbers** in the list below which are **factors** of 42.

 5   **4**   **6**   **3**   **22**   **7**   **8**

13. I drank **1 . 8 litres** from a **2 litre** bottle of water.

 How many **millilitres** are left ?   _____mls.

14. If **three ninths** of a number is **18** what is the number ?   _____

15.

CONTENTS
72 sweets

David ate **27 sweets** out of the jar. What **fraction** (simplest form) of the sweets in the jar did David eat ?

Answer _____

16. How many **times** is the **7** in **73 . 4** greater than the **7** in 6 . **71** ?   _____times

17 & 18.   A drawing of a **regular hexagon** is shown below. The vertices of the shape have been joined to the centre to create 6 **equal** triangles. Where the triangles meet at the centre the 6 **angles are equal**.

17. How many degrees are there in **Angle A** ?

 _____°

18. a.   How many degrees are there in **Angle B** ?

 _____°

 b.   What is the name of a regular polygon that has **5 equal sides** ? _____

19 to 25. **Read the passage and answer the questions.**

Mr. and Mrs. Brown first met Paddington on the railway platform. In fact that was how he came to have such an unusual name for a bear, for Paddington was the name of the station.

It was a warm day and the station was crowded with people on their way to the seaside. Trains were whistling, taxis were hooting, porters were rushing about. There was so much shouting that Mr. Brown, who had seen him first, had to tell his wife several times before she understood.

"A **bear** ? On Paddington Station ?" Mrs. Brown looked at her husband in amazement. "Don't be silly, Henry. There can't be !"

"But there is," he insisted. "Over there, behind those mailbags. It was wearing a funny kind of hat."

He pushed her through the crowd, round a trolley laden with chocolate and cups of tea, past a bookstall and through a gap in a pile of suitcases.

"There you are," he announced, pointing towards a dark corner. "I told you so! "

Mrs. Brown made out a small furry object in the shadows. It seemed to be sitting on some kind of suitcase and around its neck there was a label with some writing on it. It said, PLEASE LOOK AFTER THE BEAR. THANK YOU.

"Why, Henry," Mrs. Brown exclaimed . "I believe you were right after all. It **is** a bear !"

Underline the correct word in each of the 3 sentences below.

19. a. Mrs. Brown thought her husband was **foolish, funny, excited** when he said he had seen a bear.

b. Mrs. Brown was **delighted, frightened, amazed,** when she saw Paddington Bear.

c. Mr. and Mrs. Brown were **on the railway platform, in the waiting-room,   at the ticket office.**

20. Name **three sounds** that could be heard at the station.

_____   _____

_____

21. What was the bear **wearing** when Henry first saw it ?

_____   5.

22. At **what time** of the year do you think the story took place ?

_____

23. Write down **one piece of evidence** to support your answer to the previous question.

_____

24. What kind of nouns are **mailbags,** **suitcases,** **seaside,** **bookstall.** Circle your answer.

proper   compact   compound   pronoun

25. **Complete the following sentences.**

a.   The railway station was crowded with people because _____

_____

_____

b.   Mr. Brown had to tell his wife about the bear several times

because _____

_____

26. How many **quarter kilogram** bags of sweets can be filled from a carton of sweets which weighs **4 and three-quarter Kgs** ?   _____bags

27. A bag of potatoes weighed **12 Kgs**.
A greengrocer took **3.4 Kgs**. and
2.65 Kgs. out of the bag.
What weight of potatoes was left ?   _____Kgs

28. In 6 days of postal deliveries a postman delivered 64 letters on Monday, 57 on Tuesday, 42 on Wednesday, **80 on Thursday,** 68 on Friday and on the Saturday 49 letters.

What **fraction** of the letters were delivered on **Thursday**. Give your answer in **lowest terms**.   _____

6.

29 to 32.

This is the Bus

Timetable from

Belfast to Dublin.

BELFAST --- DUBLIN

Belfast dep.	..............08:00
Lisburn	..............08:50
Portadown	..............09:20
Armagh arr.	..............10:15
Armagh dep.	..............10:35
Newry	..............11:25
Dundalk arr.	..............12:15
Dundalk dep.	..............12:30
Drogheda arr.	..............13:25
Drogheda dep.	..............13:55
Dublin	..............14:50

What is the journey time from :-

29. Belfast to Armagh ?   _____ hrs. _____ mins.

30. Armagh to Dundalk ?   _____ hrs. _____ mins.

31. Lisburn to Newry ?   _____ hrs. _____ mins.

32. Belfast to Dublin ?   _____ hrs. _____ mins.

33 to 36. **This is the Calendar for the month of March 2008.**

MARCH	2008					
Sun	Mon	Tues	Wed	Thurs	Fri	Sat
						1
2	3	4	5	6	7	8
9	10	11	12	13	14	15
16	17	18	19	20	21	22
23	24	25	26	27	28	29
30	31					

33. On what **date** was the **2nd Friday** of March 2008 ?   _____

34. What was the **date** of the day **one week** after the 16th March 2008 ?   _____

35. On **what day** of the week was the 26th February 2008 ?   _____

36. On **what day** of the week was the 6th April 2008 ?   _____

7.

37 to 41. Read the poem and answer the questions.

Spreading oak, reaching out to enfold nature,   *line 1*
Stretching up from the heavens, to show strength   *line 2*
above all others,   *line 3*
Below your umbrella - like branches,   *line 4*
Young people cuddled in each others arms,   *line 5*
protected by your magnificent foliage,   *line 6*
Some hide behind you to shield their bodies   *line 7*
from others,   *line 8*
birds nest in your brances to bring forth   *line 9*
new life for nature,   *line 10*
Insects, butterflies and ivy, all find a common   *line 11*
bond with you,   *line 12*
People tattoo your bark with messages of love.   *line 13*
Sometimes hate,   *line 14*
Even politics.   *line 15*
So you see, spreading oak, you are to us a   *line 16*
house, a leaning post,   *line 17*
A writing pad, a changing room, a bird   *line 18*
sanctuary,   *line 19*
A calender, a reminder, and an umbrella.   *line 20*
A beautiful part of our lives.   *line 21*

Tick (√) the correct answers below.

37. The **noun** which is a **plant** and the **noun** which is the
adult of a caterpillar are in

A   line 1 ☐   B   line 4 ☐

C   line 11 ☐   D   line 16 ☐

38. In **line 11** you'll find the words **ivy, butterflies** and **insects**.
What **"part of speech "** are these words ?

A   verbs ☐   B   nouns ☐

C   pronouns ☐   D   adjectives ☐

39. The word **from** is used incorrectly in line 2.
Which of the following is the **correct word** for this line ?

A   with ☐   B   on ☐

C   to ☐   D   after ☐

40. A **spelling mistake** and a **missing capital** letter are to be found in

A   line 4 ☐   B   line 7 ☐

C   line 9 ☐   D   line 18 ☐

41. The word **calender** is spelt incorrectly in **line 20**.
Which of the following is the **correct spelling** ?

A   callendar ☐   B   calendar ☐

C   calandar ☐   D   calander ☐

Write the **missing numbers** in the spaces.

42.   _____ x 10 = 2340

43.   275 ÷ _____ = 2.75

44. Joan gets **£2** pocket money each week.
She saves **one fifth** of it. In how many
weeks will she have saved **£2.80** ?   _____ weeks

45. Underline the **shortest** length.

5.1 m   51 cm   511 mm   0.5 m

9.

46. A patio measures **200 cms** long and **500** cms wide.
What is the **area** of the patio ?
Tick (√) your answer.

   1.0 sq. metres ☐   10 sq. metres ☐

   14 sq. metres ☐   100 sq. metres ☐

47. How many $\frac{1}{10}$'s are there in **4.8** ?   _____ tenths

48. Write 77,400 grams in **kilograms**. Tick (√) your answer.

   77.4 kgs ☐   7740 kgs ☐   7.74 kgs ☐   774 kgs ☐

49. Write the missing number.

   6^2 + _____ = 62

50. Write the **correct answer** to the following calculation:-

   If **4 x f** = **11** then **12 x f** = _____

51. What is **40%** of **£250** ?   £ _____

52 to 58. **Read the passage and answer the questions.**

   Montreal is a very large city, but, like all large cities it has some very small streets. Streets, for instance like Prince Edward Street, which is only four blocks long. No one knew Prince Edward Street as well as did Pierre Dupin, for Pierre had delivered milk to the families on that street for thirty years.
   During the past fifteen years Pierre's milk wagon had been drawn by a large white horse named Joseph, who knew the route as well as Pierre. Pierre used to boast that he did not need reins - he never touched them. Each morning Pierre reached the stable of the milk company at five o'clock. The wagon would be loaded by him and Joseph hitched to it; then this splendid combination would stalk proudly down the street.

52. What **kind of a word** is Prince Edward Street ?
Tick (√) your answer.

   compound noun ☐   proper noun ☐   pronoun ☐
                        10.

53. What is **unusual** about all large cities ?

_____

54. Why did Pierre state that he **didn't need reins** for Joseph ?

_____

55. Which **word** best describes Pierre's horse ?
Tick (√) your answer.

jealous ☐   strong ☐   faithful ☐   friendly ☐

56. Which **word** best describes Pierre's relationship with his horse ?
Tick (√) your answer.

fragile   trustworthy ☐   strong ☐   uneasy ☐

57. Write **True** or **False** for each of the following :-

a. Pierre loaded the milk on to the wagon..........._____

b. Joseph and Pierre were together for 30 years.._____

c. Pierre started work at five o'clock..................._____

d. Joseph was a dark brown horse....................._____

58. This is a **summary** of the passage. In the summary there are
groups of **three words** from which to choose.
Underline the **most appropriate** word from each group which
makes the summary an **accurate** version of the passage.

The **town   country   city** of Montreal has **no   a few
many** small streets which have their own names. The
milkman had delivered milk on these streets for **fifteen
twenty   thirty** years while his companion Joseph had
worked for him for **fifteen   twenty   thirty** years.

11.